ALL KINDS
OF NEIGHBORS

A Little Owl Book 🦉 Holt, Rinehart and Winston, Inc., New York

All Kinds of Neighbors

by Howard R. Wellesley

illustrated by Aliki

Copyright © 1963 by Holt, Rinehart and Winston, Inc.
Library of Congress Catalog Card Number 63-15202
Printed in the United States of America
03-023760-2

0123 60 98765

There are all kinds of neighbors.

Some neighbors talk out the window.

Some do not.

Some neighbors make loud noises.

Some do not.

Some neighbors always hurry.

Some do not.

Some neighbors plant flowers.

Some do not.

Some neighbors play outdoors.

Some do not.

Some neighbors feed the birds.

Some do not.

Some neighbors give parties.

Some do not.

Some neighbors bake cookies.

Some do not.

Some neighbors work all the time.

Some do not.

Some neighbors ask you to come in.

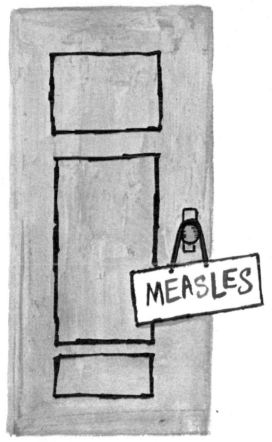

Some do not.

What kind of a neighbor are you?